THE 7 HABITS

of Highly Effective Network Marketing Professionals

Stephen R. Covey

Manjul Publishing House

First published in India by

MANJUL

Corporate and Editorial Office

• 2nd Floor, Usha Preet Complex, 42 Malviya Nagar, Bhopal 462 003 - India

Sales and Marketing Office

• 7/32, Ground Floor, Ansari Road, Daryaganj, New Delhi 110 002 - India
Website: www.manjulindia.com

Distribution Centres
Ahmedabad, Bengaluru, Bhopal, Kolkata, Chennai,
Hyderabad, Mumbai, New Delhi, Pune

Copyright © FranklinCovey Company

The 7 Habits of Highly Effective Network Marketing Professionals
by *Stephen R. Covey*

Franklin Covey and the FC logo and trademarks are trademarks of
Franklin Covey Co. and their use is by permission.

FranklinCovey India and SouthAsia
JIL Tower A, Institutional Area,
Ground Floor, Plot No. 78, Sector-18,
Gurgaon, Haryana - 122 001 India Tel: +91 124 4782222
Mumbai: +91 22 42754444, Bangalore: +91 80 40716888
Website: www.franklincoveysouthasia.com

This edition first published in 2016

ISBN   978-81-8322-740-7

Printed and bound in India by Thomson Press (India) Ltd.

All rights reserved. No part of this publication may be reproduced, stored in or
introduced into a retrieval system, or transmitted, in any form, or by any means
(electronic, mechanical, photocopying, recording or otherwise) without the prior
written permission of the publisher. Any person who does any unauthorized act
in relation to this publication may be liable to criminal prosecution
and civil claims for damages.

Table of Contents

Introduction.. 5

Three-Person Teaching 7

Paradigm Shifts... 9

Victories: Both Private and Public............................. 13

Habit 1: Be Proactive.. 15

Habit 2: Begin With the End in Mind...................... 20

Habit 3: Put First Things First................................... 25

Habit 4: Think Win-Win.. 30

Habit 5: Seek First to Understand,
            Then to Be Understood................................ 35

Habit 6: Synergize... 40

Habit 7: Sharpen the Saw.. 44

INTRODUCTION

You are not your habits; thus, you can make or break your habits. You do not need to be a victim of conditions or conditioning.

Habits are patterns of behavior composed of three overlapping components: knowledge, attitude, and skill. Because these three components are learned rather than inherited, our habits constitute our second nature, not our first. Thus, we can make or break our habits. Habits of effectiveness can be learned, habits of ineffectiveness unlearned.

Timeless Principles

The 7 Habits are based upon timeless principles. Principles are guidelines for human conduct that are proven to have enduring permanent value. Just as there are natural laws, such as gravity, that govern the physical dimension, principles are natural laws that govern the human dimension.

Habits are powerful factors in our lives. Because they are consistent, often unconscious patterns, they constantly express our character and determine our effectiveness—or ineffectiveness. Breaking deeply imbedded habitual tendencies that violate basic principles of human effectiveness involves a tremendous effort. However, once we break these habits, our freedom takes on a whole new dimension.

Like any natural force, gravity pull can work with you or against you. The gravity pull of some of your habits as a network marketing professional may be keeping you from going where you want to go. But it is also gravity pull that keeps your world together. It is a powerful force, and if you use it effectively, you can use the gravity pull of habit to create the cohesiveness and order necessary to establish effectiveness in your business and your life.

Making Commitments

This application workbook is organized into two sections: summaries of the presentation and application exercises. Read the summaries in the workbook and complete the application exercises as you progress through the it. These exercises provide you with the opportunity to make the commitments necessary to live the 7 Habits.

Three-Person Teaching

If you knew you were going to teach this material tomorrow, say to a very important group of people, would that affect the way you learn today?

—Stephen R. Covey

You learn best by teaching other people.

When we teach someone else what we have learned, we learn twice: once when we receive, and again when we give. Receiving begins the learning process; teaching someone else completes it. We learn more completely when we teach someone else. Our attention can't wander. We can't get by with partial understanding. Knowing that we have to teach someone else makes us more alert when we are being taught. For these reasons, we encourage you to teach the material contained in *The 7 Habits of Highly Effective Network Marketing Professionals* to someone else on your team. We call this Three-Person Teaching. You are one; the person who teaches you is two; the person whom you teach is three.

Three-Person Teaching has at least three additional benefits. First, it broadens your perspective. You can't live solely within your own way of thinking—you must fit what you know into someone else's way of thinking. Second, you make a social statement. You put yourself on the line. You are seen as someone who is learning and growing. Third, teaching helps lubricate change. When you teach someone, that person will be more likely to make allowances as you put forth efforts to change. This first Three-Person Teaching exercise takes effort. Commit to do it. Few things will help you and your team more than sharing what you are learning with others.

APPLICATION EXERCISE
A 48-Hour Teaching Commitment

This is a long-range application exercise that covers your entire experience with The *7 Habits of Highly Effective Network Marketing Professionals*. Your goal is to teach someone else on your team what you learn. We suggest that you share the concepts within 48 hours. You'll benefit and so will the person who listens to you. At your first opportunity, tell this person (or people) what you intend to do. This will affirm your commitment. To help you get started please answer the following questions:

1. Whom will you teach?

2. When will you share with this person your intention to teach him or her?

3. When will you teach the material to this person?

Paradigm Shifts

We all see the world not as it is, but as we are. We look through our own frame of reference, the paradigm of our whole past background and experience.

—Stephen R. Covey

If you want to make small improvements, work on behavior and attitudes; if you want to make major improvements, shift your paradigm (how you see the situation and your role in it).

The Power of Paradigms

The word "paradigm" means a model, pattern, or set of ideas that describes some aspect of the world. Paradigms are basically mental images you have in your mind of the way things are out there. A simple way to understand paradigms is to see them as maps. Maps show us where things are and how they relate to one another. When we move to a new city, a map helps us get around. After a while, we may throw the map away, replacing it with a more complicated and detailed mental map. The more we move around, the more complete our mental map—our paradigm of the city—becomes. Likewise, you create paradigms of prospects, team members, your company, etc. You even create paradigms of yourself.

The Social Mirror

Some of our most important paradigms are the ones we hold of ourselves. These paradigms come, in part, from the "social mirror." The social mirror is what other people say about us and how they react to us. It is their perceptions, opinions, and paradigms about us. From this social mirror come our self-maps—our images and judgments of ourselves, such as "I'm not good at talking to prospects" or "I'm good with presentations."

The social mirror is based on our memory of how other people have treated us or reacted to us. Our potential, on the other hand, is what we imagine we might become. Because the information we obtain from the social mirror is based on what other people think about us, it can be wrong or only partially correct. In a sense, what we see in our imagination as our potential can actually be a more correct picture of what we're like than reflections of the social mirror.

Our Paradigms Affect Other People

We affect other people through the paradigms we hold of them.

The social mirror is a two-way mirror. Just as other people are our social mirror, we are theirs. By being aware of that relationship, we can use the principle of the social mirror to encourage people to expand their limits rather than to live within them. If we live from memory only—if we remember and reflect people's mistakes and weaknesses—we may influence them to repeat the same mistakes. On the other hand, if we see other people's potential and reflect what we see, we may help them move toward their potential.

Our paradigms of other people may cause the problems we blame on others.

Whenever you have problems with another person, whether it's a prospect or an upline or a downline member, it's wise to consider the possibility that your paradigm of him or her could be contributing to the problem. Because paradigms create their own evidence and filter your understanding, you may be seeing problems that aren't there, or you may be seeing them as bigger than they really are.

APPLICATION EXERCISE
Your Paradigms of Other People

Consider the following comment by Stephen R. Covey:

"Think about the key relationships in your life—your loved ones, your work associates, etc. What paradigms do you have of these people? Is it possible that your paradigms are the source of a problem? We all see the world not as it is, but as we are."

With that in mind, take a few moments to reflect on a relationship you have with another person in your business that isn't going as smoothly as you'd like. Consider the following questions:

1. Reflect upon your paradigm of the other person. Have you labeled him or her? In what way?

2. Is it possible that your paradigm could be the source of the problem?

3. How might you change your paradigm to improve the relationship?

4. How might you alter your actions in the relationship so the other person might also grow and change?

Victories:
Both Private and Public

The 7 Habits provide a sequential approach to move you progressively from dependence to independence to interdependence. They represent, first, a Private Victory, and second, a Public Victory. Habits 1, 2, and 3 will lead you to Private Victories—the victories that allow you to achieve self-mastery and dominion over self. Habits 4, 5, and 6 lead you to Public Victories—victories that allow you to achieve success with other people. The habits form a continuum because the Private Victory precedes the Public Victory. Until you have developed self-mastery, it is difficult, if not impossible, to achieve success with other people. Together, these 7 Habits cultivate personal character, which is the very foundation of effectiveness.

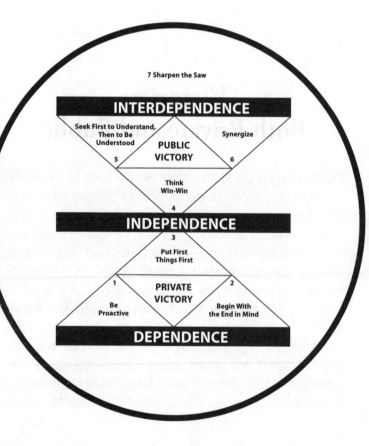

Habit 1: Be Proactive

The Habit of Personal Vision

Anytime you think the problem is out there, that thought is the problem. You have just empowered what's out there to control you.
—Stephen R. Covey

Proactivity vs. Reactivity

Proactivity is the power to choose
our own responses.

The first habit of highly effective network marketers is proactivity. To Be Proactive as a network marketer is to take initiative, but it means more than that. It means that you are responsible for the results you get in life. It means that you choose your own way; it isn't chosen for you. It means that you have the responsibility and the resourcefulness to make things happen. When you are proactive, you understand that your circumstances do not control you. On the contrary, you control them.

When we are not proactive—when we are reactive—we are controlled by our circumstances. Reactive network marketers see only roadblocks and difficulty. They blame outside influences and shift the responsibility to anyone or anything other than themselves.

When we are proactive, we do not blame people or circumstances for what happens to us. We believe that whatever we are or have to do is what we have chosen. Proactivity and reactivity produce different outcomes. Proactivity produces results; reactivity produces excuses or explanations. When you are proactive in your network marketing business, you see that excuses don't profit you, and you determine to be satisfied only with results.

Proactive Language and the Circle of Influence

When we're proactive, our language changes.

One way to tell if we're being proactive is to notice how we talk. We hear reactive phrases all the time. For example, a new downline member who says, "I can't go to the weekly meeting; I can't make the necessary arrangements," is implying that there is no choice, as though the task of making arrangements forces the decision not to go. It would be more accurate—and more proactive—to say, "I choose not to go to the weekly meeting because I prefer to use my time tonight to follow up with a prospect I met today." When we consciously choose to speak proactively, we remind ourselves that we are free, responsible, value-driven people.

We can divide events and circumstances into two categories: (1) those things we can affect by our choices, either directly or indirectly—the Circle of Influence—and (2) those things we cannot affect at all—the Circle of Concern.

When we are proactive, we focus on results. We concentrate on the Circle of Influence because we can only produce results within that circle.

When we are reactive, we are not interested in producing results, we are interested in producing reasons. We focus on the Circle of Concern because we can make it the reason we are not producing results.

When we work within our Circle of Influence, we don't worry that we can't influence things that lie within our Circle of Concern. Instead, we use our attitude, actions, and strategies of influence to achieve our goals despite them.

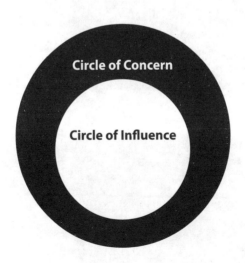

APPLICATION EXERCISE
The Circle of Influence

INSTRUCTIONS: Your goal for this application exercise is twofold:

1. To discover the situations in which you may be thinking "if only" thoughts (Circle of Concern).
2. To begin to shift your focus to the Circle of Influence.

Pick a problem within your business that is frustrating to you and write it down.

1. Identify any "if only" thoughts or reactive language you might use to escape responsibility for the problem (e.g., If only I had more people to talk to; If only I had more time to prospect).

2. If you were to follow those thoughts, where would they lead you?

3. What might you do to work within your Circle of Influence in this situation? How might this benefit your business?

APPLICATION EXERCISE

1. Try the 30-day proactivity test: Work within your Circle of Influence. List a number of small commitments regarding your business and keep them. Be part of the solution, not part of the problem. Work on things you have control over. Work on you. Track your results at the end of the 30 days.

2. Imagine an experience or an encounter in your business where, based on past performance, you might behave reactively. Decide in advance what your proactive response will be, then exercise that choice in the actual situation.

3. Pick one day a week for four weeks and listen to your language. Are you using reactive language—"If only," "I can't," or "have to"—to transfer responsibility for your feelings and actions to somebody or something else? If so, start using more proactive, positive language, expressing your ability to choose your response and to create alternatives.

4. Identify what lies within your Circle of Influence. Concentrate your energy and efforts on these things, and monitor the difference it makes in your performance.

Habit 2:
Begin With the End in Mind

The Habit of Personal Leadership

Once you really know what is deeply important to you, you've automatically got guidelines. You can manage your life each day to be and do what matters most.

—Stephen R. Covey

Values and Rescripting

All things are created twice—first mentally, then physically.

Just like blueprints for a home, there's a mental or first creation, and then a physical or second creation. If you want to have a successful network marketing business, you first clearly define what you are trying to accomplish—as an idea, a plan, an intention. Then your plan will gain physical shape through action or effort.

Begin With the End in Mind includes defining values to guide our decisions.

To Begin With the End in Mind means more than just thinking clearly about what you want to accomplish in your business. In addition to examining specific goals and plans, this habit involves looking at values and principles that give us general guidance in all areas of our lives.

Discovering Your Personal Mission

A Personal Mission Statement sets an overall purpose for your life.

Habit 2 involves creating a Personal Mission Statement. A Personal Mission Statement is the beginning of personal leadership. It sets general guidelines for your life.

Your Personal Mission Statement should contain two basic parts: vision and principles. Vision deals with the mental picture of what you are about; principles deal with how you go about it.

The most effective way to Begin With the End in Mind when it comes to success in your network marketing business and in life is by developing a Personal Mission Statement.

Organizational Mission Statements

To create great unity and tremendous commitment, form an organizational mission statement.

Mission statements are also vital to successful organizations. To be effective, that statement needs to come from deep within the organization. Everyone should participate in a meaningful way—not just upline and top leaders, but everyone. The involvement process is as important as the written product and is the key to its use.

Sample Organizational Mission Statement

The mission of our organization is to enhance the lives of those we meet through improved health and expanded opportunities.

APPLICATION EXERCISE

1. Identify an upcoming situation you will be facing in the near future and apply the principle of mental creation and rescripting. Write down the results you desire and what steps will lead to those results.

2. Start a collection of notes, quotes, and ideas you may want to use as resource material in writing your personal and organizational mission statements.

3. Set up time to completely separate yourself from daily activities and to begin work on your Personal Mission Statement.

4. Share the principles of Habit 2 with your organization and suggest that together you begin the process of developing an organizational mission statement.

APPLICATION EXERCISE
Your Personal Mission Statement

Write your Personal Mission Statement. It reflects your personal constitution, set of beliefs, or value system. It should address questions such as:

1. What is my life about?
2. What is really important to me?
3. What do I want to be?
4. What do I want to do/accomplish?

In answering these questions, use a separate sheet of paper to record insights and understandings you have about yourself. These should help you to more clearly define your mission. Clarifying your mission should be an ongoing process.

Habit 3:
Put First Things First

The Habit of Personal Management

Once you have a clear picture of your priorities—your values, goals, and high-leverage activities—organize and execute according to them.
—Stephen R. Covey

The Time Management Matrix

We gain control of time and events by seeing how they relate to our mission.

The demands on our time are either important or unimportant, urgent or not urgent. Important things serve our mission: unimportant things don't. Urgent things have a pressing deadline; nonurgent things don't.

Combining these two dimensions—importance and urgency—creates four quadrants of time demands. All time-related choices fall into one of the four quadrants. We can learn how to handle them by determining where they fall.

	Urgent	Not Urgent
IMPORTANT	**I** (MANAGE) • Crises • Pressing problems within the organization or company • Urgent applications **Quadrant of Necessity**	**II** (FOCUS) • Prospecting • Leveraging time with tool placement • Team training • Relationship building **Quadrant of Quality & Personal Leadership**
NOT IMPORTANT	**III** (AVOID) • Interruptions • Some emails • Some meetings (especially • if you don't have a guest in • attendance) • Popular activities **Quadrant of Deception**	**IV** (AVOID) • Busy work • Time wasters • Some emails **Quadrant of Waste**

We solve time management problems by focusing on Quadrant II activities.

The Time Management Matrix shows us the symptom, the cause, and the cure of time management problems.

Quadrant I is the "symptom" quadrant. It is the quadrant of urgent and important things, such as crisis management or putting out fires in your organization. All time management problems eventually surface in Quadrant I.

Quadrants III and IV are the two "cause" quadrants. Quadrant III is a vicious trap for network marketers. These are activities that appear to be urgent, but are not really important to your overriding goal as a successful network marketing professional. Similarly, unnecessary things from Quadrant IV often sap your time.

Quadrant II is the "cure" quadrant. It is the heart of personal management. In Quadrant II, we do things only because they serve our mission. They have no other urgency. We do things like build relationships, write a mission statement, do long-range planning, and focus on continuous improvement.

We solve time management problems by shifting from Quadrants III and IV—the causes—to Quadrant II, which is the cure. As we do, we can prevent some of the crises and problems in Quadrant I, thereby gaining control of our life and our business. We say no to some pressing and popular things, and we say no to some pleasurable things because more business-building important activities require our time.

APPLICATION EXERCISE
How Do I Spend My Time?

1. Fit each event of your past week in the quadrant that best describes its urgency and importance. Estimate the percentage of time you spent in each quadrant.

   - In which quadrant do you spend the largest percentage of time and effort?

   - What happens to your body, mind, and organization if you stay in Quadrant I too long?

   - Which quadrant do you spend time in when you're not in Quadrant I?

2. Examine your networking business and write down an ideal "Quadrant II day" for your business. As you write down the different activities that should fall into this category, commit to implement at least one during the coming week.

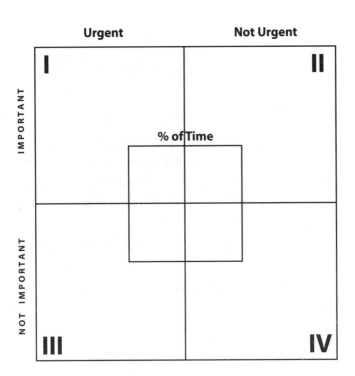

Habit 4: Think Win-Win

The Habit of Interpersonal Leadership

The win-win philosophy is not just some little technique, some nice little phrase. A win-win person has an Abundance Mentality, meaning that his or her paradigm of life is that there is plenty out there for everybody.

—Stephen R. Covey

Win-Win Means Seeking Solutions That Allow Everyone to Win

Win-win means understanding that we live in an interdependent world and must act cooperatively within it. In your network marketing business, you have to cooperate with other people in order to succeed, whether it's with prospects, team members, or even the corporate office. When you understand your interdependency, you dedicate yourself to cooperating with people in such a way that you ensure your mutual success and allow everyone to win. This is the win-win attitude.

Win-win is the opposite of the purely competitive principle that says somebody has to lose. The unique aspect about network marketing is that it is built upon a win-win philosophy. Within the realm of network marketing, there is no room for any interaction that ends in someone losing. Clearly, the key to motivating superb performance from your team is to practice a win-win mentality.

Having an Abundance Mentality means you don't see your business as a big competition and that most of your achievements don't stem from competition or comparison.

People in network marketing with an Abundance Mentality see the business as having "plenty for everybody," and they attempt to create options to help other people succeed. By rejoicing in the successes of others, they are perceived as being more successful themselves. When we admire good outside of ourselves, part of that good adheres to us. Our affirmation of others produces growth in ourselves.

Most people develop the opposite of an Abundance Mentality—a Scarcity Mentality.

People with a Scarcity Mentality see the business as a "zero sum" game, and they think that when someone else wins, in some way they lose. They think in adversarial, competitive ways. Network marketing professionals with a Scarcity Mentality do not rejoice in the successes of other people. They feel that success outside of themselves takes away from them. Their thinking is based on the assumption that there are limited resources, that there is only so much success and prosperity, and if someone else is getting part of it, then the remaining part available to them is diminished. That's why network marketers with a Scarcity Mentality seek to maintain prerogatives of positions and power, with little regard to others in their organization.

Win-Win or No Deal

The most mature attitude in a relationship is "Win-Win or No Deal."

1. **Win-win** is a frame of mind and heart that constantly seeks mutual benefit in all human interactions.

2. A primary alternative is **win-lose**, which is a self-seeking or selfish attitude.

3. The opposite of win-lose is **lose-win**. Lose-win means "I lose, you win."

4. If both people in a human transaction think win-lose, the result will be **lose-lose**, which is manifested in wars, conflicts, or other adversarial activities.

5. Another common alternative is simply to think **win**—to only think of getting what you want.

6. The sixth alternative is superior, in some respects, to win-win. It's called **Win-Win or No Deal**.

Courage and Consideration

Difficult negotiations often result when each side thinks: "How can I get what I want?" A win-win attitude changes that thought to: "How can we both get what we want?"

To go for win-win, you not only have to be considerate, you have to be courageous. You not only have to be caring, you have to be confident. To do that, to achieve that balance between courage and consideration, is the essence of effective leadership. Win-win network marketers don't really have to manage their people's performance; they set mutually beneficial expectations with their people, and the people manage themselves.

APPLICATION EXERCISE
Courage and Consideration

1. Think Win-Win means to seek mutually beneficial solutions. Identify an upcoming team meeting or prospecting activity. Determine to explore mutually beneficial options with the other people involved.

2. Identify a model of win-win thinking in the network marketing industry—someone who seeks mutually beneficial solutions even when other people may be going for win-lose. Determine what you can learn from this person's example and apply it.

3. Think about your current network marketing business. What agreements, if any, do you have in place with your team to help achieve your common goals? Is it a Win-Win Agreement? How could having such an agreement in place increase productivity within your team? Take time now to write down your Win-Win Agreements. If you do not have any, take time to create one. Review the agreement with your team during your next conference call or team meeting.

Habit 5:
Seek First to Understand,
Then to Be Understood

The Habit of Communication

Most people listen, not with the intent to understand, but with the intent to reply.
—Stephen R. Covey

Diagnose Before You Prescribe

Where does understanding begin? Demanding to be understood is a way of saying, "You open your mind for me. " Wanting to understand the other person is a way of saying, "I'll open my mind for you. "The two are so different in tone and meaning that it's hard to do both at the same time; therefore we generally focus on one or the other. Most people focus on being understood.

We can be different by seeking first to understand. When we seek to understand, we are applying the principle of empathy. We have empathy when we get inside another person's frame of reference in order to experience his or her feelings as he or she experiences them. Empathy does not necessarily mean that we agree; it means simply that we understand the other person's point of view.

Once we understand, we can proceed with the second step of the interaction: seeking to be understood. It is much more likely that we will actually be understood if we seek first to understand.

Effective network marketers are superb at listening first before they attempt to "solve" people's problems with their business opportunity or product.

Keys to Communication

- When we are open, we give people room to release their fixed positions and consider alternatives.
- Seeking first to understand lets us act from a position of knowledge.
- By seeking to understand, we gain influence in the relationship.

The Attitude and Skill of Empathy

People develop the skill of Empathic Listening in five stages.

Empathic listening combines several skills, including capturing feelings from nonverbal cues and phrasing empathic responses clearly and supportively. These Empathic Listening skills take practice.

People typically learn the skills of Empathic Listening in five stages:

Stage 1: Mimic the content of the communication. In this stage, we simply repeat what is said—words only, not feelings.

Stage 2: Rephrase content. Now we put the other person's meaning into our own words. This takes more thought than stage 1, but it also creates more awareness.

Stage 3: Reflect feelings. Here we look more deeply and begin to capture feelings.

Stage 4: Rephrase content and reflect feelings. We express both the words and the feelings and wants behind them—Stages 2 and 3 combined.

Stage 5: Learn when not to reflect. The last stage of Empathic Listening is discerning when it isn't necessary to reflect and when it may even get in the way.

Then to Be Understood

The second half of the skill of creating understanding is seeking to be understood.

Once we understand, we then proceed to be understood. Win-win is a balance between courage and consideration. Being understood takes courage. Both are necessary conditions for Win-Win Agreements.

If, in the course of being understood, we sense resistance, we have the opportunity to choose to be defensive or to seek to understand. Thus, we may find ourselves moving back and forth between seeking to understand and seeking to be understood. The process is complete when both parties feel understood.

When you can present your own ideas clearly, specifically, visually, and most important, contextually—meaning in the context of a deep understanding of their paradigms and concerns—you significantly increase the credibility of your ideas. What you're presenting may even be different from what you had originally planned because in your effort to understand, you learned.

APPLICATION EXERCISE
Achieving Mutual Understanding

1. Select one of your permanent prospects or product consumers. Make a commitment to base your next presentation to this person on empathy. Describe his or her viewpoint as well as or better than he or she would, then seek to have that person understand how your products/opportunity may positively and directly influence his or her viewpoint.

2. Share the concept of empathy with someone close to you on your team. Tell him or her you want to work on really listening to others and ask for feedback in a week. How did you do? How did it make that person feel?

3. The next time you have an opportunity to watch people in your organization communicate, cover your ears for a few minutes and just watch. What emotions are being communicated that may not come across in words alone?

Habit 6: Synergize

The Habit of Creative Cooperation

Synergy is the crowning achievement of all the habits. It leads to teamwork, team building, unity, and harmony.

—Stephen R. Covey

Value the Differences

Synergy means one plus one equals three or more.

When two or more people work together to understand something, they can create a phenomenon called "synergy." Synergy lets us jointly discover things we are much less likely to discover by ourselves. Synergy occurs when minds stimulate each other and ideas call forth ideas. For example, I say something that stimulates your mind; you respond with an idea that stimulates mine. I share that new idea with you, and the process repeats itself and even builds.

The way to create synergy is to create a context that supports it.

We can't create synergy directly. It is a by-product, and trying too hard to create it can actually prevent it. Your goal as a leader in network marketing, therefore, is to create the climate in which it thrives. The elements of that climate include a win-win attitude, seeking first to understand, and a belief in your abilities to find positive alternatives.

Synergy and Communication

Synergy is exciting. Creativity is exciting. It's phenomenal what openness and communication can produce. The possibilities of truly significant gain, of significant improvement, are so real that it's worth the risk such openness entails.

The following diagram illustrates how closely trust is related to different levels of communication.

LEVELS OF COMMUNICATION

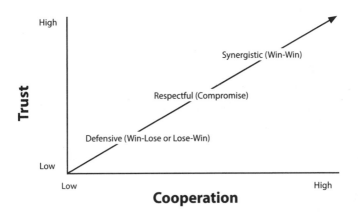

We See the World as We Are

Relationships that join people of different abilities and styles of thinking are opportunities for synergy.

Differences provide opportunities. When working relationships break down over disagreements, it is not really because of the differences, it is because the people involved did not understand the value of their differences or how to take advantage of them. Respecting differences is giving people freedom to think and considering their views as deeply as our own. Appreciating differences is seeing that they can serve us. Differences show us where our own vision is incomplete. They open windows into worlds other than our own. We can see them as a benefit or as a threat, and as we choose one or the other, we determine the quality of our relationships and the success of our business.

The Highest Skill

When properly understood, synergy is the highest skill, the payoff of all the other habits put together. Synergy focuses win-win thinking and the skills of empathic communication on the toughest challenges you face as network marketers. What results is almost miraculous, because you create new and better alternatives, solutions that didn't exist before. Synergy is the essence of effective team cooperation and performance. It's the unleashing of the greatest powers within people. All of the habits prepare you to create the miracle of synergy.

APPLICATION EXERCISE
Valuing Differences

1. Think about a person on your team who typically sees situations differently from the way you do. Keep Habit 6: Synergize and the principle of valuing the differences in mind, and list what you can do to benefit more from the differences this person presents.

2. Make a list of people inside or outside your organization that irritate you. Be honest—no one is going to see this list but you! Do they represent different views that could lead to synergy within your team(s) if you had greater intrinsic security and valued the differences?

3. Identify a situation within your group in which you desire greater teamwork and synergy. List conditions that would need to exist to support team synergy. What can you do to create these conditions?

Habit 7: Sharpen the Saw

The Habit of Self-Renewal

The only person over whom you have direct and immediate control is yourself. So the greatest assets to constantly develop, preserve, and enhance are your own capabilities. And no one can do it for you. You have to do it for yourself. It is the single greatest investment you can make because it leverages everything else.

—Stephen R. Covey

Sharpen the Saw Means Maintaining Our Personal Production Capability

Keeping tools sharp applies not only to physical instruments, but also to ourselves. We are the first instrument of our own performance. If something seems to block us, it may be because we haven't made ourselves strong enough, skilled enough, or determined enough to get over it. The problem isn't the obstacle, but the condition of the instrument. Excellent performance is a function of the excellence of an instrument. In this case, the instrument is you.

Sharpen the Saw applies a simple principle that is the key to self-directed change.

The idea behind Sharpen the Saw is to take small, positive steps every day. Doing small things consistently has a cumulative effect that is more powerful and more dynamic than any massive single effort could ever be.

Constant Renewal

Sharpen the Saw is renewing four dimensions of your nature—physical, social/emotional, mental, and spiritual. And with the high-velocity, high-profile, mile-a-minute schedule that often consumes top-level network marketing professionals, it is vital that you take the time to stop, refocus, and Sharpen the Saw.

In terms of how these four dimensions affect your networking organization as a whole, consider asking the following questions:

- In the physical dimension ask, "Are your financial needs being met?"

- And in the social/emotional dimension ask, "What about your work do you love doing? How are your relationships with others on your team?"

- In the mental dimension ask, "What are you really good at? Are your talents being used in your organization?"

- In the spiritual dimension ask, "What would make your work more meaningful to you? What contribution could you make to influence others?"

Moving in an Upward Spiral

Renewal is the principle—and the process—that empowers us to move in an upward spiral of growth and change, of continuous improvement. Once we are self-aware, we must choose purposes and principles to live by. But there is no shortcut in developing them. The Law of the Harvest governs; we will always reap what we sow—no more, no less. So we must show diligence in the process of renewal. Moving along the upward spiral requires us to learn, commit, and do on increasingly higher planes. To keep progressing, we must learn, commit, and do; learn, commit, and do; and learn, commit, and do again.

The Upward Spiral

APPLICATION EXERCISE
Sharpen the Saw

1. Commit to write down specific Sharpen the Saw activities in all four dimensions every week, to do them, and to evaluate your performance and results.

2. Teach the principle of Sharpen the Saw to your team during your next conference call or team meeting. Go through the four dimensions together and decide as a team what you can collectively do to achieve these renewal goals.